David, we're PREGNANT!

David, we're PREGNANT!

101 Cartoons for
Expectant Parents
by Lynn Johnston

OWL PRESS

© 1982, 1991 Lynn Johnston Productions Inc., and Lynn Johnston
First Published by Meadowbrook Press

Published by Owl Press, P.O. Box 315 Downton, Salisbury.
Wiltshire. SP5 3YE.   March 1993
Printed in the UK by Redwood Press Ltd Melksham, Wiltshire.

British Library Catologuing - in - Publication Data. A catalogue
record for this book is available from the British Library.

Publisher's ISBN: 0 9515917 6 2

Introduction

Once upon a time there were no cartoons on the ceiling of my surgery. From my point of view, of course, the surgery was always an interesting place where I met fascinating people, with perplexing problems for me to solve. The relationship was simple and direct. The patients had questions. I had been to medical school and learnt the answers. The surgery was the place where the questions and the answers got together. Both patient and doctor went in for the same purpose and both went out satisfied.

One day a perceptive woman, who had laid all too long on the bed counting the dots on an otherwise blank ceiling, asked me why I didn't put any pictures up there. I didn't have a good answer but I realised it was a good question. And I was struck with the realisation that the patient's point of view was very different from the doctor's. A host of new questions started to crowd in.

When does pregnancy really begin? Is it, like we were taught at school, at the precise moment when the sperm and egg join together, or is it earlier when a couple start to plan and yearn for a family? Or is it perhaps later, with the realisation of pregnancy and the growing awareness of the life within?

What is pregnancy? Is it the weight gains and the blood pressures, the morning sickness and the strange symptoms the doctor sees? Or is it the hopes and fears, the joys and tremblings, a new body to adjust to and a new shape to learn to love? Is it a time for parents to prepare for their new exciting role to come?

What are antenatal classes? A passing fad to keep patients occupied? Or an opportunity for us to learn about our bodies and ourselves, to learn the skills needed for the task ahead?

What is labour? Is it a series of uterine contractions working to dilate the cervix and expel a new baby into the world? Or is it the dreaded yet anticipated experience, unknown and unknowable, through which one must pass with only old wives' tales and untested antenatal classes as uncertain guides?

Indeed, what is the new baby? A little patient to be weighed and tested? Or a new individual who will change lovers into parents and mates into a family, with new joys and sleepless nights?

There are many books about pregnancy, but most are written from a professional's point of view. The patient's answers to these questions are rarely expressed. In this book, Lynn has given the parent's viewpoint, clearly and pointedly. For parents, for parents-to-be and for professionals too.

And now I have cartoons on my ceiling.

Dr. MURRAY W. ENKIN

13

Don't be so depressed....
Remember when getting your period was a good sign?
LYNN

I'm pretty sure that I am....
but what if I'm not.... what if
it's negative ... or nerves... or
imagination. Actually, I'm
positive I am. I'll phone
for a checkup. But what
if they tell me I'm not....
better wait another week
to make sure ..... No. Why
wait if I'm POSITIVE!...
Then again... what if I'm not....
On the other hand...
maybe..........

Lynn

17

23

28

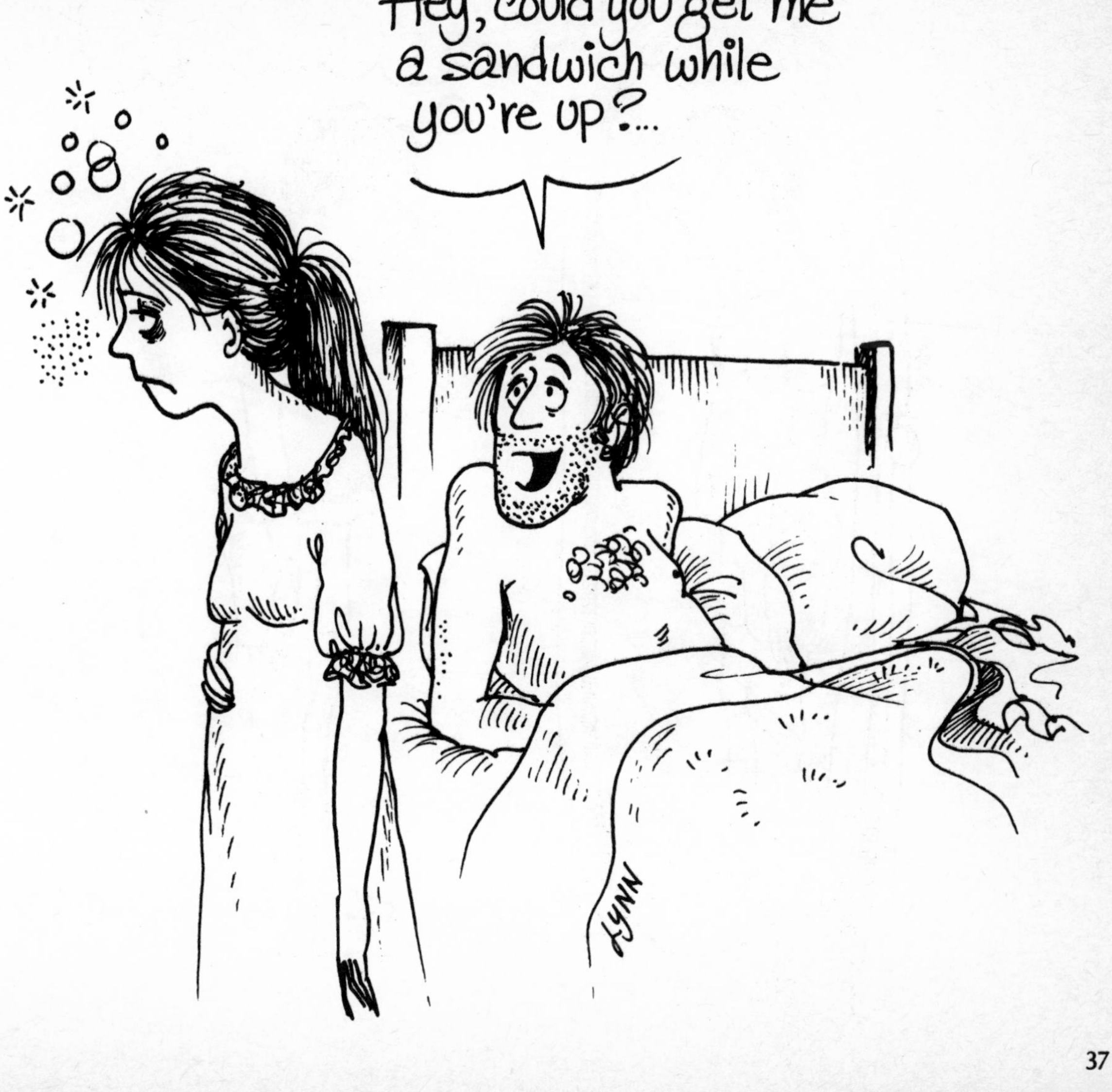
Hey, could you get me a sandwich while you're up?...
LYNN

48

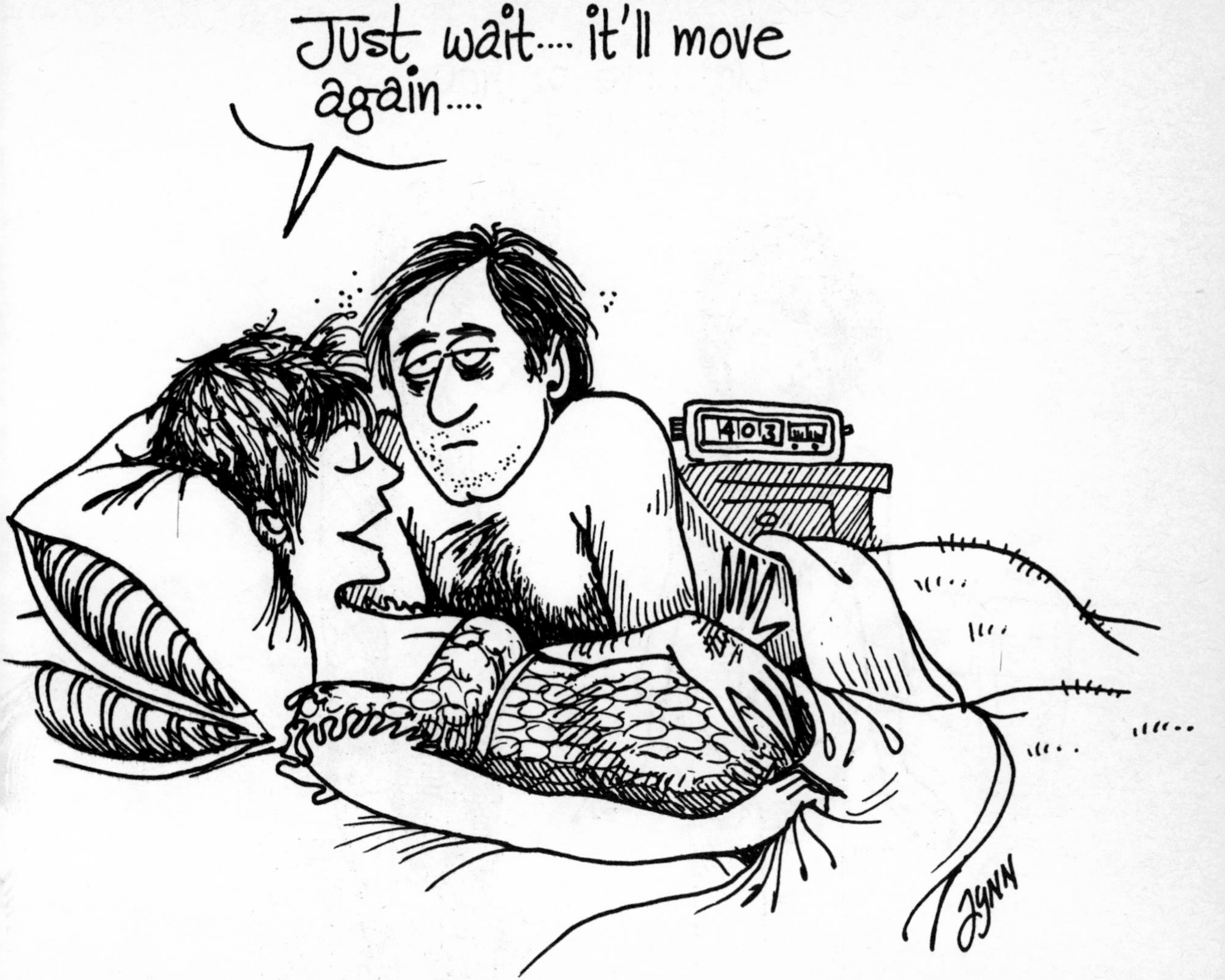
Just wait.... it'll move again....
403
LYNN

56

Mum, Ken's agreed to go to prenatal classes with Barbie....

THE LAMAZE METHOD

Lynn

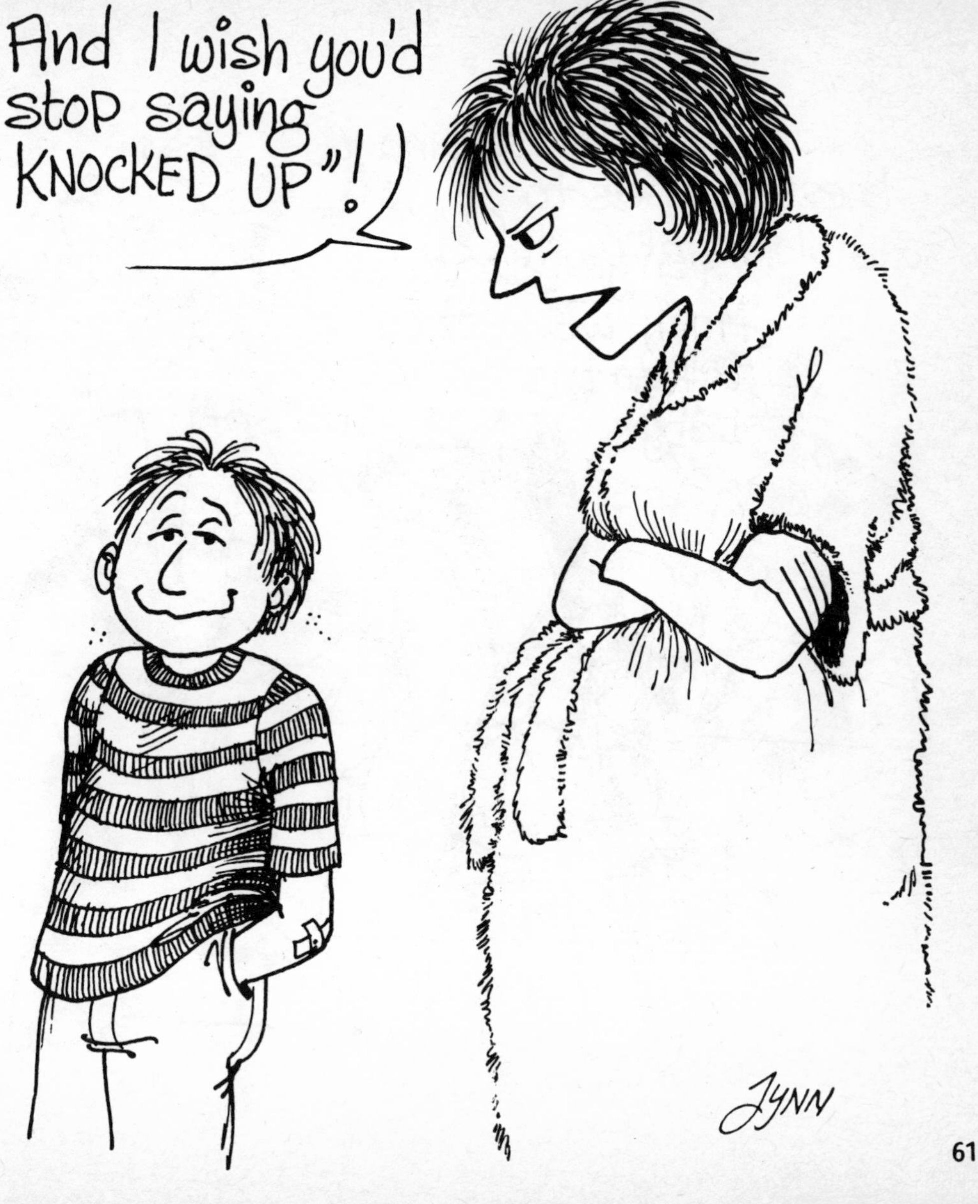
And I wish you'd stop saying "KNOCKED UP"!
LYNN

64

Mother's coming to give you the benefit of her experience....

LYNN

While you're waddling around town- could you pick me up a copy of the evening edition?

Lynn

I rather like this "Nesting Stage"!

Lynn

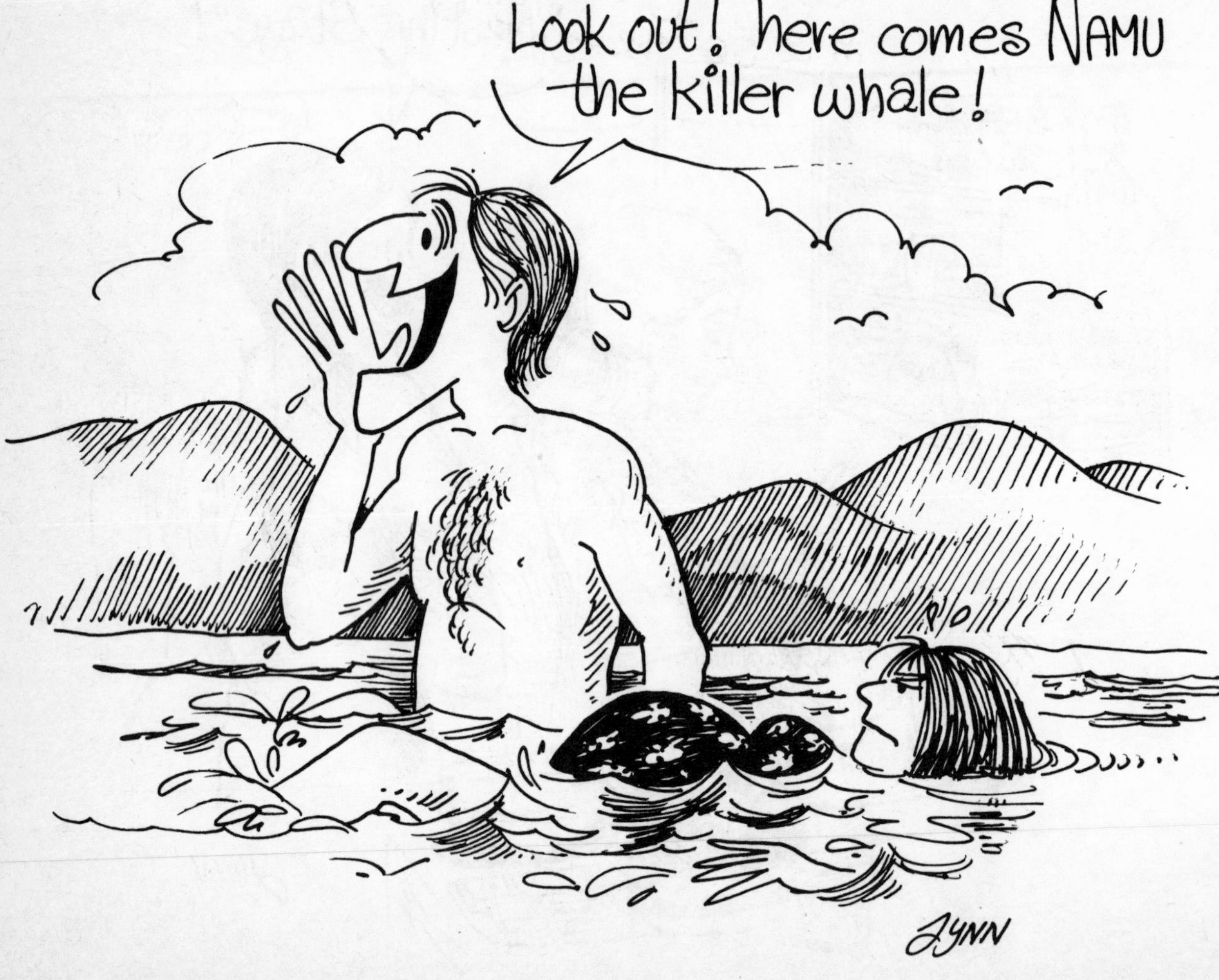
Look out! here comes NAMU the killer whale!
LYNN

No matter how I lie, I'm uncomfortable....
I think I'm going to have to learn
how to sleep standing up.
ZZZZ
LYNN

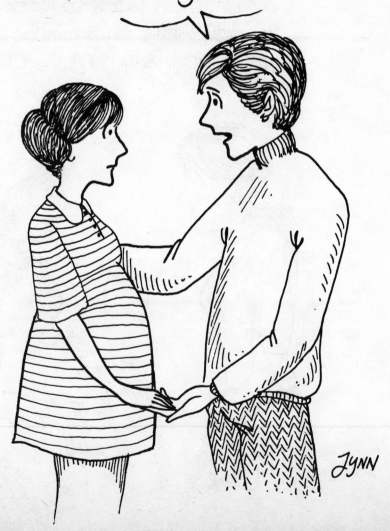

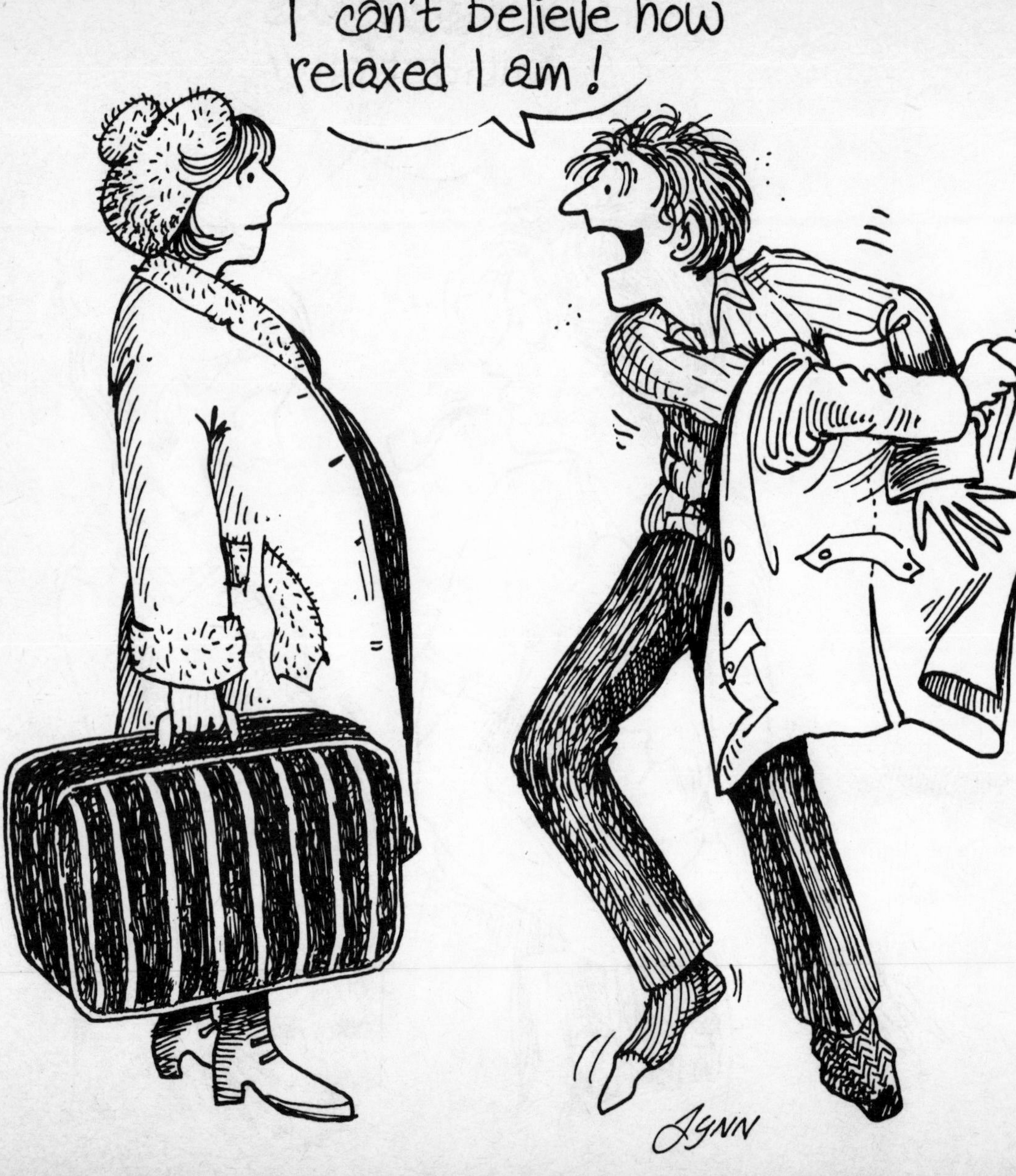
I can't believe how relaxed I am!
LYNN

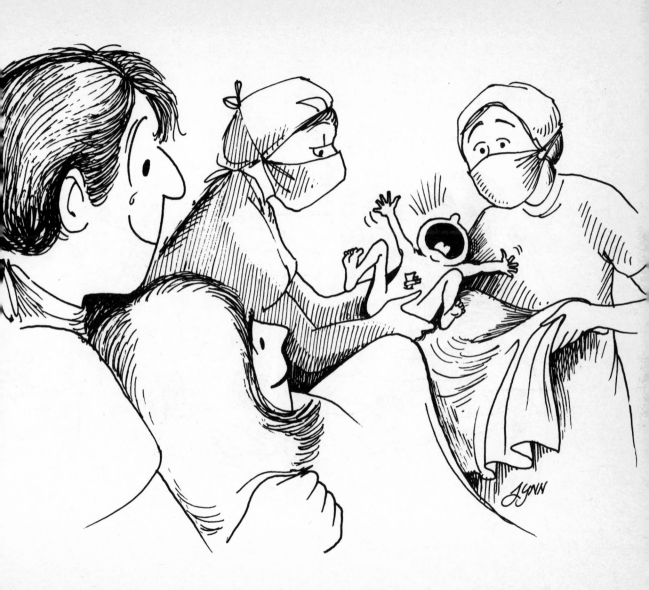

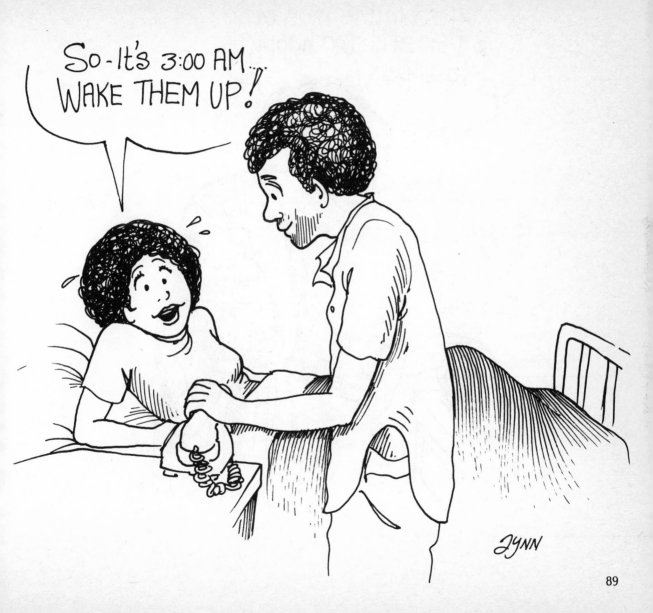

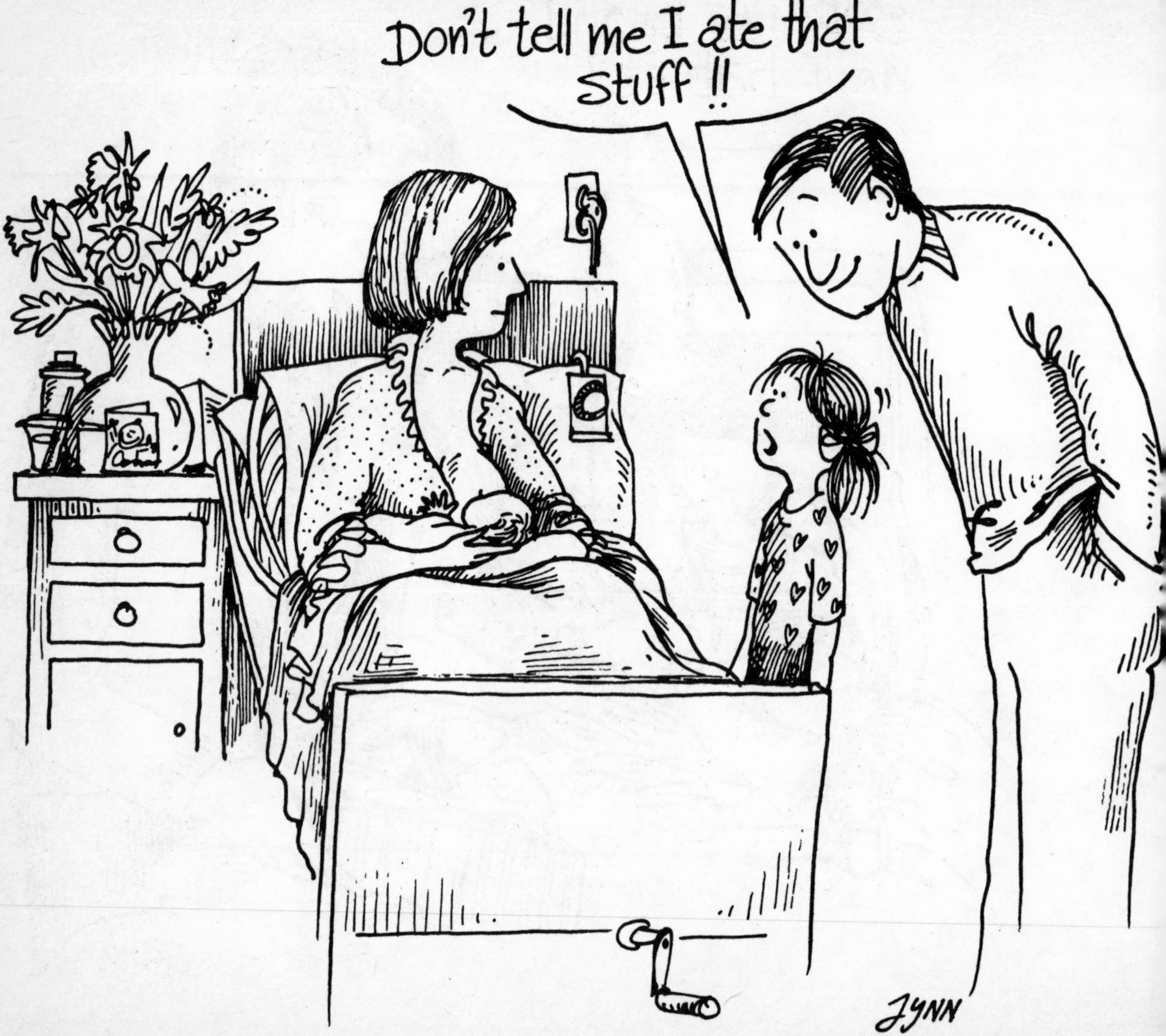
Don't tell me I ate that stuff !!
LYNN

102

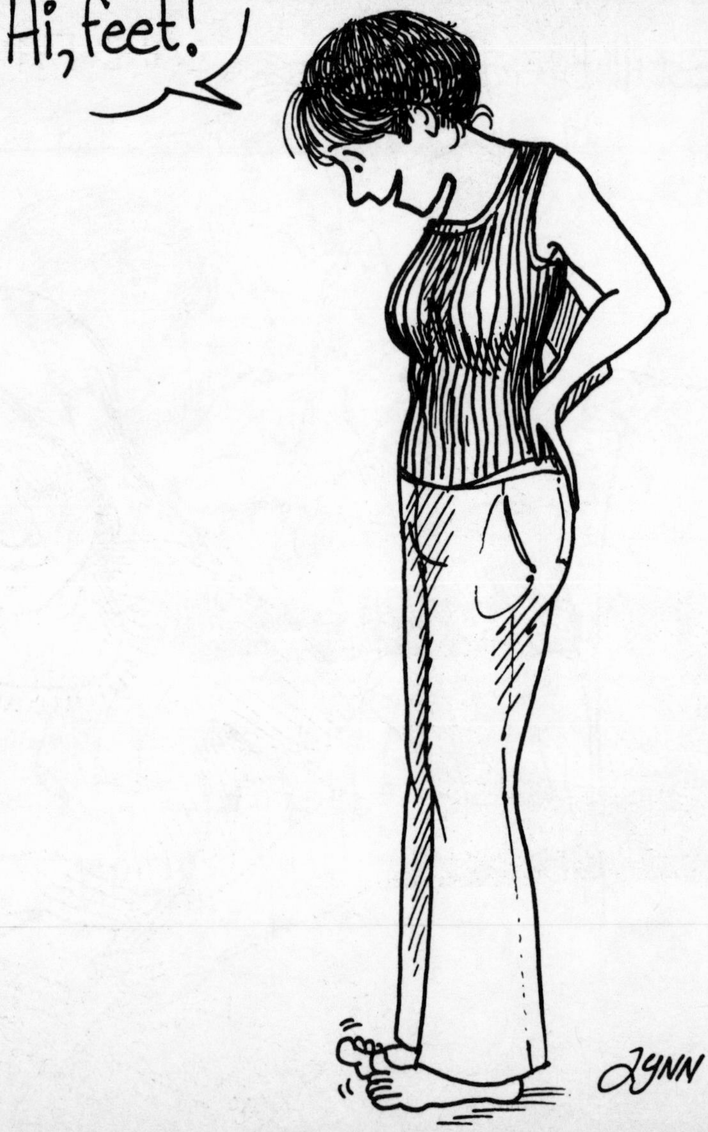
Hi, feet!
LYNN

Meet Lynn Johnston

Lynn Johnston is the world's top female cartoonist. She draws much of her material from close observation of her family. Lynn's deft, humorous depictions of life with children have provided her with material for three books published in the United Kingdom by Owl Press.

& Her Books:

DAVID, WE'RE PREGNANT!

101 laughing-out-loud cartoons on the humorous side of conceiving and giving birth. A great present, it's the perfect way to bolster the spirits of any expectant couple.

ISBN 0 9515917 6 2

HI, MUM! HI, DAD!

A side-splitting sequel to DAVID, WE'RE PREGNANT! 101 cartoons on the first year of childrearing - all those late nights, early morning wakings and other traumatic "emergencies".

ISBN 0 9515917 7 0

DO THEY EVER GROW UP?

This third in her series of cartoon books is a hilarious survival guide for parents of the tantrum and dummy brigade, as well as a hilarious memory book for parents who have lived through it.

ISBN 0 9515917 8 9